Look at the baby princess.

She is a beautiful baby.

The good fairies give presents.

Oh no, the bad fairy!

She gives a bad present.

She hurts the young princess.

It puts her to sleep.

The princess sleeps and sleeps.

"Who lives in that castle?"

Everyone is standing and sleeping.

"She's beautiful!"
He touches her…

...and she wakes up!

Everyone wakes up. "Hello!"
"Hello!"

Everyone smiles. They are happy.

Activities

Before you read

Look at the book and find a picture of ...

1. a baby 2. a horse 3. a princess

4. a fairy 5. a castle

After you read

Match

The princess is sleeping.

The princess is happy.

The king is sad.

The fairy is bad.

Pearson Education Limited
Pearson
KAO Two
KAO Park
Harlow
Essex
CM17 9NA

and Associated Companies throughout the world.

ISBN 9781292239965

First published by Librairie du Liban Publishers, 1996
This adaptation first published by
Penguin Books 2000
1 3 5 7 9 10 8 6 4 2
Text copyright © Pearson Education Limited 2000
Illustrations copyright ©1996 Librairie du Liban

Sleeping Beauty
Level 1

Retold by Nicole Taylor
Series Editor: Melanie Williams
Illustrations by Kay Dixey
Design by John Hawkins

Printed in China
SWTC/01

The moral right of the author and illustrator have been asserted

All rights reserved; no part of this publication may be reproduced, stored in a retrieval system, or transmitted in any form or by any means, electronic, mechanical, photocopying, recording, or otherwise, without the prior written permission of the Publishers.

Published by Pearson Education Limited

For a complete list of titles available in the Pearson Story Readers series please write to your local Pearson Education office or contact:
Pearson, KAO Two, KAO Park, Harlow, Essex, CM17 9NA

Answers for the Activities in this book are published in the free Pearson English Story Readers Factsheet on the website, www.pearsonenglishreaders.com